SNOW CHASE!

1. **Build** the minifigure from LEGO® elements. Now you have a Santa Claus in your collection.

2. **Read** the story about the gang of snowmen crooks and a daring police chase.

3. **Solve** the puzzles and help Officer Charlie crack the case of the stolen painting.

Police Chief Knee

I like justice—and holiday decorations!

Officer Charlie

I can make my voice sound like anybody's voice.

Hank "Gold" Tooth

I believe in Santa Claus. . . .

Willy "Crooked" Tooth

I'm older and way smarter than my brother.

Matilda "Mommy" Tooth

I'm the boss of one hundred crooks . . . All of them are blockheads.

SEARCH AND FIND

Welcome to winter in LEGO® City! Get ready for a wild and funny adventure. But before that happens, find all of the characters in the story (listed on the left) in the picture above.

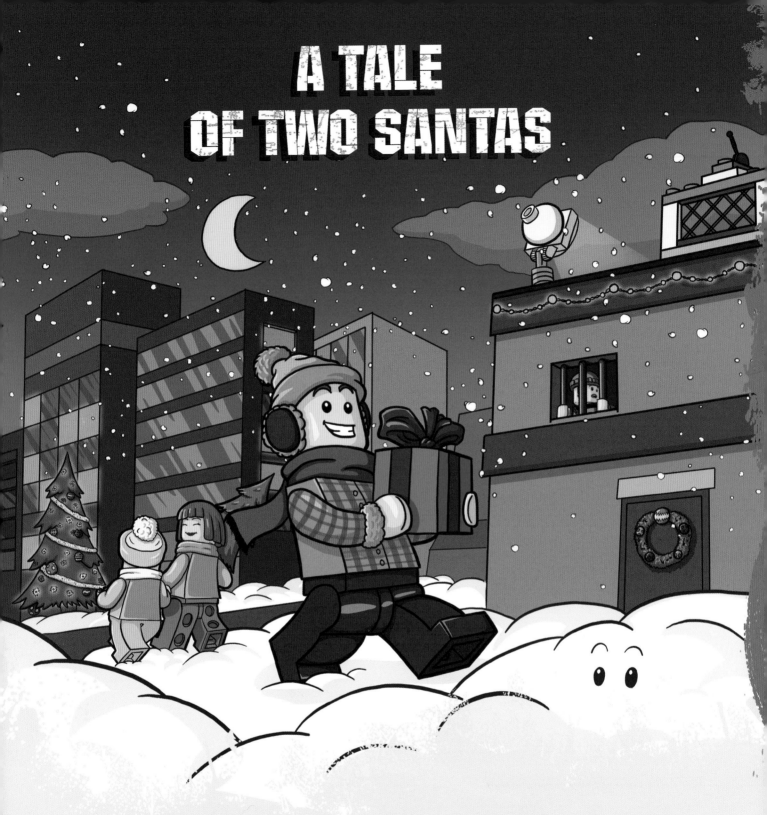

A TALE OF TWO SANTAS

Hank "Gold" Tooth leaned against the window in his jail cell. He looked outside at the snow-covered city. Next to Hank was his brother, Willy. Willy was humming to himself while he decorated a Christmas tree made out of old newspapers. Hank sighed as he admired the view.

Suddenly, Hank froze. One of the snowdrifts started to move. Then a pair of eyes blinked, and a mysterious figure emerged from the drift in a Santa suit.

"Willy, look!" Hank cried happily, running around the cell. "It's Santa Claus! Santa Claus has come to see us!"

Willy looked out the window. "That's not Santa," he said. "That's Mommy down there!" Hank was amazed. He took another look. Santa Claus removed his fake beard for a moment and flashed the famous gold smile of the queen of crooks, Matilda "Mommy" Tooth. Just then, several snowmen popped up from beneath the snow.

"It's Mommy's new gang dressed as snowmen!" Willy exclaimed. "Soon we'll be free!"

On this quiet evening, the entire LEGO City police force was decorating the station for the holidays. Police Chief Knee was just placing a star on the top of the Christmas tree when he heard someone behind him.

"Why are you decorating a tree when you should be doing police work?" a gruff voice asked.

The chief recognized the booming voice. It was the LEGO City mayor. "Uh, sorry, Mister Mayor—" the police chief stuttered, leaping from the stepladder. "It's just the holidays and I wanted to . . ."

But when Chief Knee looked around, he didn't see the mayor. Instead, Charlie and the other officers were laughing. "Where's the mayor?" the chief asked.

"The mayor isn't here." One of them giggled. "It was Charlie. He can imitate anybody's voice!"

The chief definitely wasn't laughing.

Chief Knee called Charlie over. "So, you have acting skills?" he asked.

"Yes, I do, Chief!" Charlie said proudly.

"In that case, take this Santa Claus outfit!" the police chief ordered. "Today, you'll be working in front of the police station. When anybody walks by, give them season's greetings from the LEGO City police."

"What about patrol?" Charlie whined.

"I gave you an order!" the chief said sternly. Once Charlie left, the chief returned to decorating the tree.

Meanwhile, Matilda's gang was hard at work rolling enormous snowballs. They were making a giant snowman. When the snowman was finished, Matilda used it like a ladder to reach the window of the jail cell.

"Mommy, can I build a snowman, too?" Hank asked, overjoyed.

"Don't talk nonsense!" Matilda barked. "We've got work to do. Give your brother a file and start sawing through the bars!"

In another room at the police station, Officer Charlie was putting on the Santa Claus suit. "While everyone gets to go on patrol and keep LEGO City safe, I'll be making a fool of myself dressed as Santa Claus!" Charlie grumbled.

The station alarm suddenly sounded throughout the police station. Charlie ran to check the cells where the Tooth brothers were locked up.

Unfortunately, the only thing he managed to see was the leg of one of the crooks disappearing out the window. The window bars had been sawed through and the criminals had escaped!

Charlie leaped toward the window to follow the crooks, but he forgot about his Santa suit. Instead of catching the crooks, his giant Santa belly got caught on the window frame!

"Wow, Mommy! This is great!" shouted Hank as the whole gang raced off through the snow.

"Don't talk nonsense!" Matilda snapped back. "Go faster! Here come the cops!"

"Wait for me!" Charlie called as several police cars raced after the gang. "I'm stuck!" But the sirens drowned out his cries. Charlie pushed and squeezed until finally, like a cork popping out of a bottle, he flew out the window. He crashed into the head of the giant snowman that was just outside the window. Suddenly, the whole snowman began to shake. "Oh, no!" cried Charlie. "This is not good!"

Meanwhile, the fugitives stopped in front of the LEGO City Museum. "What are we doing here?" asked Willy.

"Happy holidays!" shouted Matilda. "As an early Christmas present, you can rob the museum!"

"Mommy, this is the best Christmas ever!" Willy said.

"You're the best mother in the world!" Hank added, jumping with joy.

"Don't talk nonsense!" Matilda cried. "Get to work!" They all ran to knock down the museum door.

A huge snowball rolled through the streets of LEGO City. Officer Charlie, dressed as Santa Claus, was balancing on top like an acrobat!

"Quit playing around, Charlie!" Chief Knee shouted. "We have crooks to catch!"

"I'm trying!" said Charlie. "How do I stop?"

"Stop waving your legs around!" the chief shouted from his car.

"I tried that!" he replied. "It didn't work!"

Charlie and the giant snowball were rushing right toward the LEGO City Museum! The policeman covered his eyes just in case. When the snowball crashed into the side of the building, snow went flying in all directions!

When Charlie emerged from a mound of snow, the crooks mistook him for Matilda.

"Mommy! If this is another Christmas present, you sure overdid it with all the extra snow!"

Charlie knew right away what he would do. He looked around cautiously and then imitated Matilda's voice. "Don't talk nonsense! What are you standing there for?!" he asked. Then he pointed to the real Matilda. "And tie up that other Santa Claus right away!"

"Mommy, is that the real Santa Claus?" Hank asked.

"Yes! Let's steal his loot, too," said Charlie.

That was all the encouragement the crooks needed. The brothers picked up Matilda's sack of stolen goods and put her in the car.

Charlie hopped on Matilda's snow sled, revved it up, and shouted, "Follow me! And don't talk nonsense!"

Officer Charlie led the crooks straight into the hands of his fellow officers. Police cars swarmed and a police helicopter circled overhead. There was no escape! Once the crooks were surrounded, Charlie took off his Santa Claus beard and cap.

"Gotcha!" he shouted.

"Wow, you sure look different, Mommy," Willy said.

"It's a policeman," Hank whispered to his brother.

"Our mom is a policeman?" Willy asked, confused.

The policemen pulled Matilda "Mommy" Tooth from the car. She was red with fury. When they pulled the gag from her mouth, she shouted, "Don't talk nonsense!" That was all she managed to say before the police took her off to jail.

The policemen gathered around Charlie and congratulated him for the clever way he used his voice to fool the crooks.

The chief said, "Charlie, these are your last days . . ."

"You still haven't forgiven me for my prank earlier?" Charlie asked sadly.

"I was going to say these are your last days as an officer. I'm promoting you to detective!" cheered the chief.

Attention, attention! This is not the end of the Officer Charlie's adventures! Solve the puzzles and help him work out the mystery of the stolen painting!

MISSION: CLEAN UP

HURRY UP! THE WAREHOUSE WON'T DIG OUT ITSELF!

Charlie's last case ended up burying the museum and other buildings under lots of snow. Luckily, the cleaning crew is here to help! Which vehicles can help clean up the snow? Put an X in the circle next to each vehicle that can do the job.

It's time to transport the snowmen to the police station. In order to do that you need to fit all the crooks into the police cars. In the boxes above each car, write the number for two of the snowmen. But follow the police rules!

Police rules:
1. Only two snowmen fit into one car.
2. Tall snowmen can't ride together.
3. Two chubby snowmen have to ride separately.
4. Snowmen #1 has to ride in the navy blue car.

BREAK-IN

WE'LL HIDE THE PAINTING IN THE PIZZA BOX AND THEN . . . RUN!

WE'LL FINISH THE MISSION OUR BOSS, MATILDA, STARTED!

Two snowmen in Matilda's gang – Tommy and Manny – managed to escape. Now, they're trying to steal a painting of a woman from the museum. However, they don't know how to get past the lasers. Draw a line leading the robbers around the lasers and to the painting.

Manny and Tommy got out of the museum without being caught. Now, they need to find their escape vehicle. All they know is that the SUM of all the numbers on its license plate is the biggest. Can you add up the numbers on each license plate and find their getaway car?

POLICE CHASE

Some crooks are trying to escape in a stolen car. Help the police by drawing THREE barricades that will block ALL the escape routes for the criminals.

Tommy and Manny made a run for it! They tripped and fell into a giant pile of snow. Can you match each crook with his shape in the snowdrift?

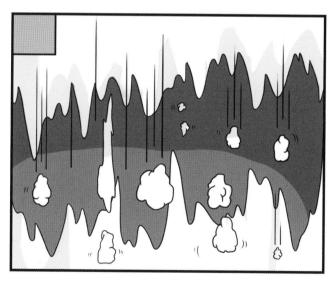

GO!

The police got bicycles as Christmas gifts. However, their first ride didn't end so well. What happened? Put the pictures in the correct order to find out.

TIMETABLE

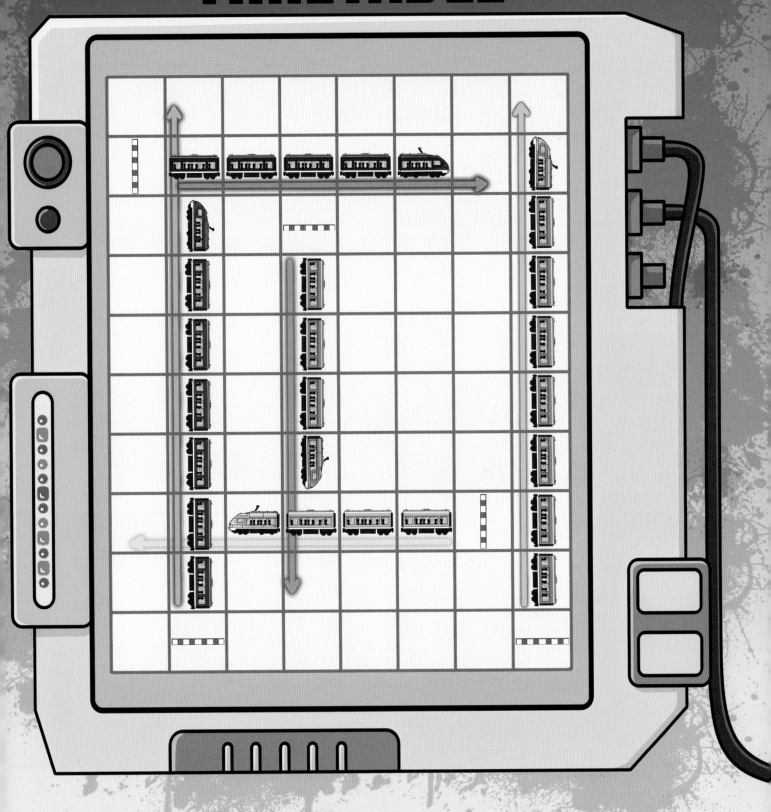

There is traffic at the railway station. A train can only move if no other train is in front of it. Can you decide which train should leave first, second, third, fourth, and fifth? Write the correct number next to each train on the next page.

CITY →

KNEE'S MISSION

1

2

A PAINTING WAS STOLEN FROM THE MUSEUM! WE NEED TO FIND IT FAST! LET'S GO!

Chief Knee is going on a secret mission and needs a mobile police unit. Compare the two vehicles above and find five differences between them. Then choose which unit has more special equipment on board for Chief Knee.

POLICE HUNGER

HIGH-ALTITUDE CHASE

Officer Charlie has almost caught up with the stolen painting! You can help by drawing a line leading him to the crooks. Be careful not to step on the cracks on the floor.

It looks like all the crooks have been captured, and the stolen painting returned. It is time for Charlie's big promotion. They're even awarding him with a big trophy for his extraordinary service. But where is he? Find him! Hurry up! Chief Knee is already waiting!

ANSWERS

page 3 — SEARCH AND FIND

page 13 — MISSION: CLEAN UP

page 16 — BREAK-IN

page 14-15 — DESTINATION: POLICE STATION

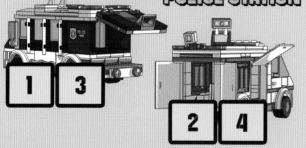

page 17 — HELP NEEDED

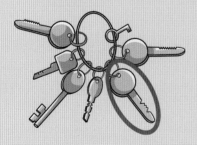

Missing shovel
from Page 13

page 20 — POLICE CHASE

Sample Solution

page 18 — RUN!

GH4034

4+0+3+4=11

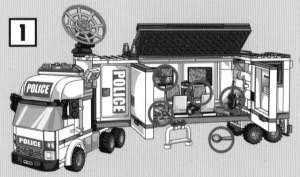